P9-CQA-988

WILD PLANTS IN FLOWER

Trientalis borealis *Star Flower* PRIMULACEAE

Around the globe at the northernmost reach of forest cover, the woods is one—a circumpolar expanse of evergreens called, from Greek mythology, after *Boreas*, personification of the North Wind. Under the boreal forest's dark canopy spreads a ground layer of flowering species themselves conspicuously similar across Old World and New. One such, with a close "cousin" in Eurasia, is *Trientalis borealis*, widespread in mixed and coniferous woods from Yukon to Labrador.

FROM NATURE

by TORKEL KORLING

WILD PLANTS IN FLOWER

II

The Boreal Forest and Borders

WITH NOTES
ON THE SPECIES
AND THEIR DISTRIBUTION
by EDWARD G. VOSS

DUNDEE · ILLINOIS · 1973

Familiarity with habitat preferences of forest floor wild flowers permits a "read-out" of soil and microclimatic factors that shape larger forest regions. ON THE COVER: Seedlings of the evergreen BALSAM FIR canopy (see page 11) emerge from a mosaic of GROUND DOGWOOD (pages 52, 68), MARSH FERN, WILD SARSAPARILLA (pages 14, 24), and CLUB-MOSS (pages 9, 52). Sharp eyes will find more.

First printing, 1973.
WILD PLANTS IN FLOWER: The Boreal Forest and Borders.

Torkel Korling, Dundee, Illinois 60118.
Library of Congress Catalogue Card Number 72-91541.
Printed in U.S.A.

BOREAL FOREST AND BORDERS

The boreal forest is that great circumpolar north woods common to Canada, northern Europe and Siberia. Called by the Russian plant geographers *taiga*, this is the farthest-north-reaching cover of continuous trees, giving finally onto the barren ground of *tundra* at what amounts to "timber line" on the continents themselves.

Such a line approximated on vegetation maps is the expression of an essentially climatic boundary: irregularities locally reveal topography's effects on micro-climate. Similarly, but less conspicuously, climatic factors impose the limits and create the exceptions to the reach of boreal forest southward.

In North America, the boreal formation's southern limit is generalized as a line southeasterly from Alaska to the Great Lakes, and east through the St. Lawrence valley into northern New England. What this demarcation means, any visitor to north woods can learn to "read" in the vegetation he walks through: a gradual change in composition, through disappearance of some species and increasing occurrence of others.

In some situations, however, a border may be crossed that is strikingly distinct. Just as individual plants mingle at the scale of a single site, so, through border country at large, whole stands of boreal vegetation may be found isolated amidst more temperate forest types. Innumerable such southern outliers today remain as relicts of once more extensive boreal influence. Northern vegetation has been perpetuated since the retreat of the glaciers by climate-modifying complexities of local relief or exposure.

Transition between zones of vegetation may be revealed in mingling of individuals or of whole communities. The circumboreal BEECH FERN here (*Thelypteris phegopteris*) may, like some relict boreal stands, be holding its own in an area of ecological advantage, or may be on its way to elimination by competitors genetically suited to changing conditions. CANADA MAYFLOWER (*Maianthemum canadense*, seen with other associates on pages 14 and 24) prospers in forest clearings, is abundant through all but wettest woods of northern North America.

Boreal relicts may persist on sites cooled *directly* by soil moisture in areas of blocked drainage, or *indirectly* by the thermal buffering of nearby open water. Growing conditions "northern" enough to support boreal forest thus still may be encountered locally in bogs, hollows, and around lake shores throughout the glacier-formed landscapes from Canada south into Minnesota, Wisconsin, Michigan, New York, Vermont, New Hampshire and Maine.

Farther south, the equivalent of northern conditions prevails at higher elevations, and so both Rocky Mountains and Appalachians, even into the Smokies, encompass zones of boreal vegetation.

Whether maintained by altitude or local microclimate, such discontinuous relict stands differ little in tree canopy and herbaceous ground layer from the forests of the geographic North. Deliberate public acquisition has preserved many of these sites for education and research. Most are open to visitors. Here one may literally go, with a few steps, into the forest of the far North, or the distant past.

As the last glaciers retreated thousands of years ago, regions of exposed rock, melting ice, and accumulated gravels again became available for colonization by plants and animals. Underfoot in today's north woods may still be found evidence of stages in the plant succession by which such mineral soil became habitable. In the growth form and habit of many typically northern plants are clues to the limitations that still persist.

The evergreen habit permits forest trees and mosses maximum activity in the short northern summer. It gives the same advantage to flowering species of the ground layer. *The trailing habit* of some low woody perennials lets them deploy working leaves over any available surface, often literally carpeting logs, stumps, mossy hummocks—even sand blows. *The creeping habit*, with colonies formed of off-shoots from underground stems (rhizomes), accounts for similarly dense leafy carpets of many herbaceous species. Less obviously, *specialized nutrient-gathering relationships* provide many plants necessities otherwise unavailable. Lichen is a textbook example: notable among others are Heath and Orchid Family members.

Two evergreen-leaved, trailing, Heath Family representatives meet on common ground at this cedar and balsam fir forest edge. Especially characteristic of the boreal forest is the tiny-leaved *Gaultheria hispidula*, whose inconspicuous flowers develop by mid-summer into the white fruits that give it the name CREEPING SNOWBERRY.

Trailing Arbutus / *Epigaea repens* / ERICACEAE

One of the most wonderfully fragrant of all our wildflowers. Blossoms, varying from white to pinkish, appear in April and early May, often nearly hidden beneath the leaves. The species is widespread in eastern North America, south to the Gulf states. The northern variety, ranging almost to Hudson Bay, is characteristic of dry, often coniferous woods.

Trailing Arbutus

Sweet Coltsfoot

The *climax* species of any forest canopy and ground layer are those that can perpetuate their kind in the environment dictated by the dominants. In the north woods, this means year-round *shade* under the evergreen canopy, and the *acid soils* formed in a climate where even scant organic litter, due to *coolness* often compounded by *wetness*, finds biological decomposition retarded. The eventual dominants are species of SPRUCE (*Picea*) and FIR (*Abies*, the branch here at bottom). Depending upon local conditions of succession, either or both may be joined by or replaced by other deciduous or evergreen shrub or tree species. Logging, fires, storms or other setbacks may favor stands of ALDER, ASPEN, BIRCH, POPLAR or PINE. Bogginess may give TAMARACK (*Larix laricina*) a virtually permanent place in the association, limestone gives the advantage to ARBOR VITAE (left, above, here; *Thuja occidentalis*). Higher latitudes or altitudes see fir give way to spruce. Characteristics that may give *Petasites*, opposite, a place in the climax are its large light-gathering leaves, and reproduction by creeping rhizomes or wind-carried seeds.

Sweet Coltsfoot / *Petasites frigidus* / COMPOSITAE

Unlike most members of its family (daisies, asters, goldenrods), this plant flowers not in fall but in earliest spring, before its leaves are fully grown. The leaves (one just opening, center) might remind one of MAY-APPLE leaves; they are often abundant in the summer, when flowering heads are no longer evident. The stem leaves are quite different, and anatomically represent flattened leaf stalks. The seedlike fruits develop beneath a tuft of silky white hairs, a parachute for dispersal. This is a circumboreal species in the broad sense, but North American plants, var. *palmatus*, are often recognized as a separate species, *P. palmatus*, which ranges from Labrador to Alaska, south to northern New England and the Great Lakes region.

THE BOREAL FOREST IN NORTH AMERICA

The boreal forest was what I found when as a boy I bicycled to the edges of our town on the west coast of Sweden. In the years since, I have never been long away from that same forest's edge in North America. Natural vegetation everywhere has done considerable retreating in our lifetimes. This book, as will each one in the series, WILD PLANTS IN FLOWER, aims to provoke an appreciation for what remains, whether you can recollect what once was or not.

In the preparation of this volume we have been fortunate to have the help and cooperation of Dr. Edward G. Voss, Professor of Botany and Curator in Vascular Plants at the Herbarium, University of Michigan. He is Editor of *The Michigan Botanist*, and an active member of the Michigan Natural Areas Council, working to locate and evaluate sites for preservation. Part I of his *Michigan Flora* was published in 1972 by Cranbrook Institute of Science. Accompanying the illustrations here are notes by Dr. Voss on the species and their distribution, and on the remainder of the text, Mrs. Korling has consulted with him.

In the border country between the United States and Canada, where the limits of the boreal zone drop south around the Great Lakes, are some of the most accessible examples of this world-wide north woods, and happily, often the richest in wild flowers. Some of the reasons why are made clear in the BACKGROUND provided here by Dr. Voss, as introduction to the main section of the illustrations.

Torkel Korling

The glacier left behind not only a raw land surface on which spruce and fir and associated northern herbaceous plants became established. It also left the basins, originally shaped by earlier glaciations, in which the entire Great Lakes system developed. From the mouth of the St. Lawrence River almost halfway across the North American continent, some 300,000 square miles are in the drainage basin of the Great Lakes—about a third of this area being the waters of the Lakes themselves. These lakes have had a complex history, in times past draining via the Mississippi River rather than the St. Lawrence; across the Grand River valley of Michigan, or across the Ottawa Valley of Ontario.

Among the reasons for the long-term changes in Great Lakes levels and their drainage patterns are two major factors: blockage of outlets during advances of the glacial ice and continuing gradual uplift of the earth's crust upon relief from the great burden of the glaciers—which may have been a mile or two thick at their maximum. This "rebounding" of the earth's crust has been greater farther to the north, so that in the northern Great Lakes region the early postglacial shorelines are now tilted from south to north (the shoreline of an old lake stage is higher, for example, on Mackinac Island than it is at Green Bay).

The resulting apparent lowering of the lake levels has left in many places a remarkable series of old beach ridges roughly paralleling the present shore. For the past two and a half thousand years, the Great Lakes system has been relatively stable, so these ridges have been established for hundreds of years. Sometimes there are belts of old sand dunes, and sometimes flat meadows or marshes between, just as there may be beach pools along present shores.

Evidences such as these of the history of the Great Lakes may be seen today in many scenic resort and recreation areas. Some of these are Wisconsin's Door Peninsula (in Lake Michigan opposite Green Bay), with its Ridges Wild Flower Sanctuary; Mackinac Island, and

Goldthread

Wilderness State Park, on the Straits between Lakes Michigan and Huron; and the Bruce Peninsula of Ontario, in Lake Huron opposite Georgian Bay—all rich sites for wild flowers in season.

While there is not complete agreement among botanists and foresters as to terminology for the transitional forests of mixed hardwoods and conifers such as we have in the northern Great Lakes region, the important point for readers of this book is clear: most of the plants included are at or near the southern limits of their range when we find them in or bordering the coniferous woods of the northern United States. Visitors, as it were, from yet farther north, they are thus mostly unfamiliar to residents of the deciduous forest or prairie regions.

But if we travel north for refreshing coolness in the summer, we cross a climatic and floristic border zone, however indistinct, into the eventual predominance of such northern plants. Adapted to the complex of northern climate and northern soils, they are unable to thrive farther south.

Goldthread / *Coptis trifolia* / RANUNCULACEAE

A circumboreal species, the plants of northeastern North America and Greenland sometimes recognized as *Coptis groenlandica*. *Coptis* flowers from May into June; the shiny leaves are evergreen—see page 68. Its common name comes from the slender bright golden yellow underground stems (rhizomes). Its associates, here in bud and early leaf, seen blooming on page 24, are all representative of the boreal forest.

The soils of the northern coniferous forests are generally acid, and the fallen needles of the conifers help to maintain the acidity. But where the underlying rock is limestone (or dolomite) and is at or near the surface, conditions may not be acid.

Examples of what this means to the landscape may be followed along the Niagara Escarpment. This formation, bared by glacial scouring, is seen on geologic maps as an arc from Niagara Falls and the Bruce Peninsula, northwest across Manitoulin and Drummond Islands in northern Lake Huron, west through the Upper Peninsula of Michigan, and down again to the Door Peninsula of Wisconsin. Other limestone formations are exposed elsewhere, yielding the calcareous gravel and pebbles of many Great Lakes shores. Even beach sands may be partly calcareous. Where there is a source of carbonates, aquatic plants may deposit beds of marl.

Thus, where the ever-moving waters of the lakes have, over the centuries, eroded cliffs of limestone or piled up ridges of limey gravel, conditions prevail quite unlike the acid ones created under the influence of coniferous woods elsewhere. The WHITE-CEDAR, ARBOR VITAE, and a diversity of other plants are often characteristic of these locales.

The Great Lakes have influenced plant distribution in other ways. These massive reservoirs of water also have a "refrigerating" effect along the immediate shores. Snow melts last in the spring under the constant shade of the conifers here. Breezes from the lakes keep even the summer temperatures perhaps 20° lower than prevail just inland.

Birdseye Primrose / *Primula mistassinica* / PRIMULACEAE

Locally abundant in damp calcareous meadows along Great Lakes shores, also on cliff faces, in rock crevices, along marly riverbanks and sheltered river valleys. The species is found from Labrador to eastern Alaska; similar Primroses of the Old World form a circumboreal complex. This one is at peak of bloom in May; it was first described as new to science by the French botanist and explorer André Michaux, who found it at Lake Mistassini in northern Quebec in September of 1792, as the snows were already beginning to fall.

Birdseye Primrose

Dwarf Lake Iris

Although most of the plants in these pictures may be expected through vast areas of boreal forest and its southern outliers, some may be developed at their best, or are most likely to be seen, at the borders of the coniferous woods fringing northern lakes.

The little LAKE IRIS, characteristic of old calcareous beach ridges now slightly shaded by conifers, here meets CREEPING JUNIPER, *Juniperus horizontalis*, often found blanketing open sand dunes and upper beaches. This low evergreen shrub is also found along the Atlantic coast and west to Wyoming and Yukon. In the Great Lakes region, it is, like the Iris, largely restricted to the shores.

Dwarf Lake Iris / *Iris lacustris* / IRIDACEAE

First described as new to science from Mackinac Island, where it was found in 1810 by Thomas Nuttall, a Philadelphia naturalist who made the first scientific excursion through the Straits on his way west, this is now recognized as an endemic species of the Great Lakes region. It grows nowhere else in the world but near the shores of northern Lakes Michigan and Huron, from Ontario's Bruce Peninsula to the Door Peninsula of Wisconsin. Its nearest relative seems to be the DWARF CRESTED IRIS, a southern species.

Included here can be only a small selection, some of the conspicuous and interesting among the hundreds of kinds of plants known from the depths and borders of the northern conifer forests. The references on page 71 may help to put names on those *not* pictured, and to feed the further curiosity this brief sampling may provoke.

Bead-lily

In the notes accompanying the illustrations, each plant is identified by scientific name (according to Gleason and Cronquist's *Manual*), and one of its common names. Remarks on habitat and blooming season pertain particularly to the boreal forests around the Great Lakes.

The arrangement of species approximates their coming into bloom, from spring through fall. Seasons vary, of course; plants vary from place to place within a season. And there are always those individuals which bloom earlier or later than expected, due to innate genetic constitution or to the conditions of climate or soil in which they happen to be situated. Some of the regional guides among the references may be helpful. But the observer cannot sit down in the woods, book in hand, and expect blooming to progress like clockwork. Accept these wild plants in flower wherever and whenever you find them. Blessed indeed is the person fortunate enough to find all of these in bloom for his personal admiration and pleasure.

Edward G. Voss

Bead-lily / *Clintonia borealis* / LILIACEAE

An important species of the boreal forest, widespread in coniferous, deciduous and mixed woods across northeastern North America. *Clintonia* honors DeWitt Clinton, early 19th century governor of New York. Its pale yellow flowers account for the common name CORN-LILY; BLUE-BEAD-LILY refers to the berries, true blue in color, which ripen in summer and are perhaps even more striking than the blossoms of May and June. The berries are sometimes suspected of being poisonous, but there seems to be no documented evidence for or against their edibility.

The Orchid Family, sometimes popularly thought of as tropical and epiphytic, is well-represented by terrestrial species of both wet and dry north woods: see pages 40-43 and 60-67.

Behind every successful orchid, it appears, may be one or more species of fungus. Via underground connections, by-products of the fungi become inputs to the orchid plant, vital through every stage of development. The subtleties of such relationships may defy even well-intentioned attempts to cultivate orchids, and remain a focus of interest to students of orchid ecology.

Specializations similarly elaborate, and easier for the non-specialist to recognize, are those of orchid flowers, for cross-pollinization by insects. Species of bees, wasps, flies, moths and mosquitos are among those identified as pollinators of North American orchids, with floral structures often precisely matched to the insect's form and habit. Until pollinated, orchid flowers may remain fresh for days or weeks; can you detect signs of age here?

Fairy-slipper / *Calypso bulbosa* / ORCHIDACEAE

A circumboreal species, widespread at higher elevations in western North America, where it was a favorite of the great Sierras naturalist John Muir. Eastward across the northern Great Lakes into northern New England, it is local, usually in rather dense coniferous woods, including hummocks in cedar swamps. Its single basal leaf survives the winter, and is replaced by new growth after the flower of May or June. Sepals and lateral petals usually are magenta or pale purple, sometimes apricot or pure white.

Fairy-slipper

 Wild Sarsaparilla

Now identifiably blooming are the plants first in evidence among the GOLDTHREAD, page 14: STARFLOWER, CANADA MAYFLOWER, and WILD SARSAPARILLA. From individual plants favorably established, any one of these may spread, by underground rhizomes, to form a part of the characteristic northern forest carpet—see Cover.

The scientific name *Aralia nudicaulis* refers to the "naked stem" of the flowering stalk. There is no stem bearing both flowers and leaves, as in two other common species of *Aralia*, and in *Panax*, closely related. *P. quinquefolius*, AMERICAN GINSENG, is of similar aspect, but the flowering umbel is borne *on* one of the stems of the foliage canopy, and develops to *red* fruits. DWARF GINSENG, *P. trifolius*, with yellow fruits, bears a tiny umbel, from a leafy stem, *above* the foliage.

Common names reflect the many frames of reference brought to botany in the New World. Chinese magical use of roots from similar species gave a name and Asian market to GINSENG; SARSAPARILLA was first a refreshing drink from the root of a tropical *Smilax*.

Wild Sarsaparilla / *Aralia nudicaulis* / ARALIACEAE

Wide-ranging across North America, to well south of the Great Lakes, Wild Sarsaparilla is a typical component of the boreal forest, especially in drier sites with some admixture of deciduous trees. Its stout horizontal roots, which contribute to the formation of large colonies, have another property, evident upon bruising or cutting. Their spicy fragrance reminds us that this is one of the native plant ingredients in root beer. The bluish-black fruits may sometimes be mistaken for blueberries—which grow on low *woody* shrubs of the Heath family, and are never in stalked spherical clusters. *Aralia* fruits may not be poisonous, but are hardly recommended, especially compared to blueberries!

Fancied resemblances yield still other common names. Annual scars on the rhizome of *Polygonatum* species, furrowed like impressions in wax, apparently account for their being called SOLOMON-SEAL. Is it perhaps chagrin, or a failure of imagination, then, that prompts a transplanted people to call so many species of a new territory simply "false" or makeshift versions of the real thing elsewhere?

As the common name here smugly points out, *Smilacina trifolia* is *not* a SOLOMON-SEAL. The "true" ones have flowers that dangle from beneath the leaves of an arching stem (as with *Streptopus*, page 31)—those of *Smilacina* are always in a terminal cluster.

To complicate the matter, the leaves and flowers of this little plant *do* resemble those of other Lily Family members (page 20, page 7). But it is *not* a BEAD-LILY: both *Clintonia borealis* and the white-flowered *C. umbellulata* of southern distribution bear their flowers in *umbels*, and their leaves have along the margins some distinctive very fine pale crumpled *hairs*—this inflorescence is a *raceme*, and these leaves are completely *smooth*. Finally, this is *not* the CANADA MAYFLOWER: both plants bear flowers in a raceme, but those of *Maianthemum* are *four*-parted, these *six*-parted; the leaf of *Maianthemum* is *heart*-shaped at its base, this *tapering*.

False Solomon-seal / *Smilacina trifolia* / LILIACEAE

One of three species of *Smilacina*, the genus itself named for a resemblance to *Smilax*. This one is often three-leaved, as the name suggests, but the number is far from consistent, ranging from one to four. Our smallest *Smilacina*, this is a circumboreal species of black spruce muskegs and other boggy places, blooming in May or June.

False Solomon-seal

Gay-wings

Seasonal peaks of wildflower bloom may be expected, but cannot always be predicted—as organizers of spring wildflower treks and field trips well know. The coming-into-bloom of any species will reflect the latitude and altitude of the site, the particulars of that year's weather, and the very local factors of topography and exposure that determine the net effect incoming sunlight and moisture will have. Thus blooming dates come to be stated with honest imprecision, as for GAY-WINGS: "May and June."

In a less sheltered spot than here, "fallen stars" on the leaves and ground might already mark the completion of flowering for *Trientalis*. In cooler depths, the BUNCHBERRY seen in bloom with *Clintonia*, page 20, could be yet to open—see page 52. Emerging buds of a SHINLEAF (*Pyrola* sp.), center, suggest a return visit to this station to find later-flowering species still.

Gay-wings / *Polygala paucifolia* / POLYGALACEAE

Other names for this little plant are BIRD-ON-THE-WING, FRINGED POLYGALA and FLOWERING WINTERGREEN: the leaves do over-winter, taking on a patina of reddish-bronze. Because of the flower's bilateral symmetry and rich color, it is sometimes hastily assumed to be an orchid, but is actually one of the showiest of the Milkworts, nowhere near the Orchids in relationship. It ranges through eastern North America, occurring farther south (in the Appalachians) than many of the other plants here, and not so far north (into Saskatchewan, beyond Lake Superior). It meets the familiars of the boreal forest under dark conifers or in sunny openings around the Great Lakes, as here in a glade of WHITE-CEDAR or ARBOR VITAE (*Thuja occidentalis*).

Conspicuous and attractive fruits in summer may lead the north woods visitor to identify members of the herbaceous Lily Family. For any north woods plants that bloom before the vacation season peaks, the developing and ripening fruits may serve as better recognition characters than flowers.

Enthusiasts tempted to eat any part of a wild plant, however, would do well to check their identification with an authority. Lacking one of the taxonomic references here (page 71), a skeptical review of other evidence is suggested. If the clear red berries of this TWISTED-STALK are so excellent, why hasn't some bird or animal taken them? The name "scoot berries," out of country wisdom, suggests a reason. Action more or less cathartic is reported for fruits of *Streptopus*, *Maianthemum*, *Smilacina* and *Clintonia*, although green vegetative parts of some, when young, are on lists of pot-herbs and may be found browsed in spring.

Rosy Twisted-stalk / *Streptopus roseus* / LILIACEAE

Its clearly "twisted" and *branching* stems (except for one variety on the West Coast) serve to distinguish *Streptopus* from both false and true SOLOMON-SEALS, which always have unbranched stems. *S. roseus* may be encountered through all kinds of northern woods, often abundantly in clearings. Flowers, in late spring or early summer, range from deep rose to pale pink. Similar but less common, tending to grow in damper, even springy places, is *S. amplexifolius*, a truly circumboreal plant found also in Europe and Asia. Greenish-white in flower, it has leaves more strongly clasping, distinctly paler beneath, and without the fringe of tiny cilia which border the leaves of *S. roseus*. Fruits of both are *red*, in contrast to the similarly borne *blue* berries of true SOLOMON-SEAL

Rosy Twisted-stalk

Twinflower

Scientific names, couched in Latin, serve to provide identification more certain than that of the common or folk names in any local language. The second name, or species epithet, often is a commentary on some physical characteristic of the plant, its typical location, or, as here, geographical distribution. Names of species *or* genus, or both, may acknowledge discovery by or simply pay honor to some particular person. In the references on page 71, the Lawrence *Introduction to Plant Taxonomy* is a precise explanation of the nomenclatural rules and arrangements; *How Plants Get Their Names*, by Bailey, is informal and conversational.

This little plant was a special favorite of the great Swedish botanist, Carl Linnaeus, and he suggested it be named for him. He once wrote, with unaccustomed modesty, "*Linnaea* was named by the celebrated Gronovius and is a plant of Lapland, lowly, insignificant, disregarded, flowering for a brief time—for Linnaeus who resembles it."

Twinflower / *Linnaea borealis* / CAPRIFOLIACEAE

Especially along borders and clearings, this little plant, technically a shrub, sometimes carpets the floor of the boreal forest, its long trailing stems giving an almost vine-like habit. The pairs of pink flowers bloom in early and mid-summer; leaves are evergreen. A circumboreal species, *Linnaea* ranges southward to West Virginia, South Dakota, Utah and California, but is most at home under spruce, fir and cedar farther north.

For the walker in actual woods, plant identification may lead t
recognition of typical associations, and distinctions in habitat. Som
may be explainable in terms of local moisture or sunlight, other
only in the context of long-range successional changes, or broa
climatic influences. Some armchair study can add depth to under
standing of the direct evidence.

A complex interaction of landscape position, standing water, peat
soil, and air-entrapping moss structures may moderate tempera
tures to make *bogs* meeting-places for species otherwise expecte
farther to the south, or north. Other seemingly contradictory min
glings may be due to variations in moisture or acidity with micro
topography, or to persistence of species from earlier successiona
stages. It's enough to send one back to taxonomy!

Here leaf rosettes of *Linnaea borealis* mingle wit
the trailing *Gaultheria hispidula* and the even mor
minutely-leaved, wire-like stems of another Heat
Family member, CRANBERRY (see also page 41
over a base of SPHAGNUM MOSS. Compare associate
on pages 8 and 33, and see references on page 7

Reading the Landscape, by Mae Watts, is a highly readable an
wittily illustrated introduction to plant ecology. Curtis's *Vegetatio
of Wisconsin*, of interest to any student of vegetation or of area
sharing that state's physical attributes, presents statistical plan
ecology studies in both tabular and narrative form, and include
many historical observations. Treating with implications at th
continental and global scale is Gleason and Cronquist's *The Natura
Geography of Plants*.

Creeping Snowberry

Cinnamon Fern • Pitcher Plant

Cinnamon Fern / *Osmunda cinnamomea* / OSMUNDACEAE

This long-fronded fern ranges north in moist places from the tropics through eastern North America to Labrador and Lake Superior. Unlike flowering plants which reproduce by seeds, the ferns reproduce by tiny one-celled spores, produced in spore-cases or sporangia. The "cinnamon" of this fern consists of the sporangia, on separate long fronds which lack green leaf tissue. In the similar INTERRUPTED FERN, *Osmunda claytoniana*, which extends farther north into the boreal forest, the fertile frond has some green leaf both above and below a middle zone which bears sporangia. Both species ripen their sporangia in late spring or early summer.

Usually thought of as a bog inhabitant is the PITCHER PLANT, which also grows happily in acid sandy hollows, somewhat shaded, as between old beach ridges. The pitchers are the leaves, hollow, and densely lined at the mouth with stiff downward-pointing hairs which prevent the escape of any crawling insect or other small animal which may venture in. At the bottom, rainwater collects, enriched with digestive enzymes secreted by the plant, which slowly work on the proteins of drowned animals: the extent to which pitcher plants actually benefit from this activity is not known.

Pitcher Plant / *Sarracenia purpurea* / SARRACENACEAE

There are fewer than ten species of *Sarracenia*, and all of them are native in the southeastern United States. Only this one ranges beyond, as far as Labrador and Saskatchewan. The flowers, of early summer, have a unique umbrella-shaped style surmounting the ovary.

Mossy bogs may become finally, conditions permitting, tree-covered land. A conspicuous intermediate stage is dominated by shrubs, notably of the Heath Family (Ericaceae). One such is LABRADOR TEA, not strictly a tea at all, although the leaves can be used to make a beverage. These leaves are densely furry with woolly hairs beneath—white under leaves of the current year, rusty brown under older leaves. This may represent a moisture-conserving adaptation to the conditions of "physiological drought" imposed by the cold and acid waters of the bogs.

The Ericaceae are well represented, also, at higher elevations and in the yet farther north. Seeking to know some of the others could be a good excuse to locate a copy of Hultén's *Flora of Alaska and Neighboring Territories*, and have the further chance to see what distribution maps for a species look like.

Labrador-tea / *Ledum groenlandicum* / ERICACEAE

An early summer-blooming shrub, Labrador-tea ranges from Greenland to Alaska, south as an abundant plant in the northern spruce forests. Farther south (for example, around the Great Lakes region), it tends to be more restricted to sphagnum bogs, like so many other boreal plants. A single blooming flower cluster alongside the *Sarracenia*, preceding, suggests scale here. A closely related species of northern Europe and Asia, *Ledum palustre*, combines with this one to make a total circumboreal pattern.

Labrador-tea

Arethusa

Arethusa was a pursued nymph who, according to one story, changed herself into a tree, and reappeared as a fountain. Myth, perhaps, but understandable in terms of the karst landscapes of the Mediterranean, where waters that fall on upland forests can utterly disappear in limestone sink-holes, to emerge only far distant.

Quite opposite, much more slowly, but explainable in stages clearly visible in some north woods settings, the bogs in which the North American orchid *Arethusa* is found quite literally do turn from water into trees. A few of the participants in that process may be glimpsed here, and are properly the subjects of a volume to themselves: species of *Sphagnum* moss; CRANBERRY, here; the *Ledum*, preceding page; and other evergreen and deciduous shrubs of the Ericaceae. TAMARACK, or larch (*Larix laricina*), a deciduous conifer, may represent the climax of woody vegetation on some permanently wet sites; others may eventually be occupied by the dominant surrounding forest type—evergreen, or deciduous hardwoods.

Arethusa / *Arethusa bulbosa* / ORCHIDACEAE

Found in open bog mats, generally in sphagnum, in coniferous swamps and similar peaty situations, from New England and southern Canada through the Lakes states, becoming very rare southward. This is the only species of the genus in North America; there is another in Japan. *Arethusa* blooms a little earlier than *Calopogon pulchellus*, which often may be found in the same boggy places—this, among TAMARACKS.

Botanists are coming into agreement that this lovely orchid be known as *Calopogon tuberosus*. Whether "pulchellus" (Latin for pretty and little) or "tuberosus" (because of the bulb-like tuber from which it grows), the plant is well-named—for "Calopogon" comes from Greek words for "beautiful beard." The beautiful beard is the tuft of white, yellow-tipped hairs toward the end of the lip. In most orchids, the lip is lowermost in the flower (like the pouch of the lady-slippers); only *Calopogon* among our native orchids has the lip uppermost—where it originated. In the others, the flower is twisted 180° so that the lip is below.

Introductory sections on orchid structure are notable in Frederick W. Case's *Orchids of the Western Great Lakes Region*, along with detailed field observations on the species. Notes on pollinators of orchids, as of all species treated, are an especially interesting feature of the F. Schuyler Mathews *Field Book of American Wild Flowers*, making it worth while to locate.

Grass-pink / *Calopogon pulchellus* / ORCHIDACEAE

Rare in the boreal forest, *Calopogon* is growing here with WHITE SPRUCE, *Picea glauca*, and a common species of rush, *Juncus balticus*, in a boggy swale between beach ridges near a lake shore. Its range is southward to Florida and Texas, usually in sphagnum bogs and other wet acid places.

Grass-pink

Shrubby Cinquefoil

Other factors than bogginess may open some areas of forest to sunlight and flowering shrubs. Disease, wind-throw or lightning strike (without the spread of fire) may create just one local opening in the canopy, initiating a "gap phase succession" that includes species suited to germinate and mature in full sun. One shrub of such situations, and of damp, particularly calcareous forest border generally, is *Potentilla fruticosa*, pictured. Of similar size and aspect is another yellow flowered plant endemic to the Great Lakes region, *Hypericum kalmianum*, SHRUBBY ST. JOHNSWORT. The two may indeed grow together. But the leaves of the St. Johnswort are simple, not divided, are without hairs, and have small translucent dots which may be seen by holding one against the light. Furthermore, the St. Johnswort flowers have a very prominent tuft of abundant long yellow stamens.

Shrubby Cinquefoil / *Potentilla fruticosa* / ROSACEAE

The bright yellow flowers of this shrub make it an attractive plant in gardens as well as in the wild. It has a long blooming season in the summer. In the broadest sense (though split up by some authors) it is a circumboreal plant ranging south in North America, particularly in more or less open calcareous damp soils, throughout the Great Lakes region (and to Arizona and New Mexico in the West). We have several species of herbaceous Potentillas, most of them with similar yellow flowers, but only this single shrubby one. The leaves consist of 5 or 7 narrow and often rather silky leaflets.

A shrub of calcareous bogs, openings and swamp borders from the boreal forests of Newfoundland and Alberta south, AUTUMN WILLOW, *Salix serissima*, here meets INDIAN PAINTBRUSH at the northern reaches of *its* range, in the Great Lakes region. This willow ripens its fruit (in conspicuous catkins) later than most, the capsules splitting open to discharge their hairy seeds which are carried by the wind in mid- or late summer.

There are many species of INDIAN PAINTBRUSH in the West, where they cause botanists great difficulty in identification. All are apparently semi-parasitic. They have green leaves and can manufacture their own food, but mature only when their roots become attached to those of several possible host plants, from which are obtained water and some mineral nutrients.

Indian Paintbrush / *Castilleja coccinea* / SCROPHULARIACEAE

The colorful tops on these plants are not for the most part flowers at all, but upper leaves or bracts; the flowers, yellowish and inconspicuous, are inside. *Castilleja coccinea* has a long blooming period, from spring to fall, in damp often calcareous ground from southern states to the Great Lakes, but not as far as the boreal forest. The more northern *C. septentrionalis*, with whitish bracts, occurs from Labrador and Vermont to the Lake Superior Region, again in the West. Do not confuse these plants with "devil's paintbrush," or orange hawkweed, *Hieracium aurantiacum*, a locally abundant weed which looks like a small orange dandelion.

Autumn Willow • Indian Paintbrush

 Striped Coral-root

Still other flowering plants of the shady and nutrient-poor northern forests may be seen to "short-cut" both photosynthesis and the soil-forming processes. Most of the North American orchids require some association with a fungus underground for growth to maturity; the "saprophytic" genus *Corallorhiza* lacks leaves or chlorophyll, and depends completely upon fungal relationships for nourishment.

Established in the still-decomposing litter layer of the forest floor, its coral-like branching rhizomes are beneficially invaded by strands of the spawn of a mushroom, which may, in turn, be associated with the roots of forest trees. Three species of CORAL-ROOT, with different total distributions in the world, have ranges in North America which include the boreal and adjoining coniferous forests. Their flowering stalks, arising singly or in large clumps, may be strikingly distinct in otherwise bare ground. All are associated with fungi.

Striped Coral-root / *Corallorhiza striata* / ORCHIDACEAE

A predominantly western American species, locally abundant eastward through the Great Lakes region to the St. Lawrence area, often associated with limestone soils. *Corallorhiza striata* blooms in mid-summer. Found later, especially in mixed woods, may be *C. maculata*, SPOTTED CORAL-ROOT, a transcontinental species ranging from Newfoundland to the Pacific, south beyond the Great Lakes and in the West to Mexico. Its forms, with lip plain or spotted, include color variations from yellow through cinnamon red and brown. Earliest in bloom and most northern is the least conspicuous, the small yellow-green *C. trifida*. A circumboreal plant, it is the only representative of the genus in Eurasia, and ranges in North America from Labrador to Alaska, south in the mountains.

Here is another plant of the north woods with a reputation in beverage-making. *Geum* itself is a derivation meaning "to have a taste," and the common name is CHOCOLATE ROOT. The academic authorities, at least, are not raving about it.

Common to most Geum species is a structural feature readily noticeable after falling of the petals in midsummer. The many individual seed-like fruits into which the flowering head develops each are topped with the persistent style, which may be plumose: those of *Geum rivale* are prominently kinked, like an umbrella handle.

Water Avens / *Geum rivale* / ROSACEAE

A circumboreal plant, found in damp clearings and along ditches and stream banks from the boreal forest southward in North America to New Jersey and the Great Lakes region (farther south in the West). The reddish or purplish color of the flower comes largely from the calyx, while the actual petals are rather cream-colored. Other species of *Geum* which may be found in northern woods and thickets but which range south beyond *G. rivale* include *G. aleppicum* with bright yellow petals and *G. canadense* with pure white petals.

Water Avens

Bunchberry

Summer is a relatively brief phenomenon in the North, where spring comes late and autumn returns early. The farther north, the closer together come spring and fall, as on mountains, where heights impose the same climatic effect, and berries at the top may be ripe before those at the bottom.

And berries, indeed, are conspicuous now through the woods: by this time many of the Ericaceae, including the blueberries and the much-prized cranberry. Remember, regulations at some public preserves prohibit the removal of any plant parts, even forest litter. Here, we have hurried in its sequence the *Comandra*, with *Arctostaphylos* next page, while holding back this obviously prime-season view of *Cornus*, to permit at least the satisfaction of comparing three plants which might be confused on account of their red berries. The fruit of the *Cornus* is seen on page 68.

Bunchberry / *Cornus canadensis* / CORNACEAE

Like its larger, shrubby relative of southern regions, flowering dogwood, this little herbaceous plant has true flowers very small and crowded together at the center of conspicuous white bracts which imitate a flower. As with other dogwoods, the leaves are quite prominently veined, the veins all appearing to run to the tip. *Cornus canadensis* is widespread across North America and also occurs in eastern Asia, a similar species in northern Europe. The branch at the top left, here, is of BALSAM FIR; left foreground are shoots of a GROUND-PINE, *Lycopodium*, one of the fern allies.

Branches in the foreground and at the left here are of BEARBERRY, *Arctostaphylos uva-ursi*, a low circumboreal shrub of the Heath Family. It is common in sandy or rocky woodlands, on dunes and old beach ridges, and in similar places, where the large mats of evergreen foliage bear red fruits late in the summer. Since "Arctostaphylos" is Greek for bearberry and "uva-ursi" is Latin for the same, the plant is triply identified, though whether it really appeals to bears may be doubtful. Perhaps we should instead use its Indian name, KINNIKINICK.

The references on page 71 include one on edible, and one on poisonous plants, to spare anyone the grief of having to re-learn what bears or Indians may have known about other possibilities.

Northern Comandra / *Comandra livida* / SANTALACEAE

Usually placed in a separate genus, as *Geocaulon lividum*, and lacking a satisfactory common name, this semi-parasitic plant is easily overlooked except when in fruit. The colorful juicy fruit (in mid- to late summer) is said to be edible. The flowers, in early summer, are small, greenish, and very inconspicuous. A plant of the boreal forest, from Labrador to Alaska and south to the northern Great Lakes region, Geocaulon occurs locally near the lake shore at the edges of conifer thickets, where its roots attach to the roots of a number of different host plants. In the background of the picture is a branch of balsam fir, *Abies balsamea*, typical of its habitat.

Northern Comandra

 One-flowered Wintergreen

As you pick a path through the crumbling twigs and needles of the forest floor, stop for a look again at these turning to soil. How many seasons' accumulation is still recognizable? Where is the line between organic litter and mineral material? Shallower than you thought, probably—as cut-away exhibits at interpretative centers often are arranged to show. Blurring the distinction, but helping to make it real, is the activity of myriad life forms, plant and animal.

To the familiar burrowing mammals, add countless grubs, larvae, mites and other microscopic insects, that till and cast and enrich the layers they work through. Now see the network of fungi, and see plant roots that bring nutrients up into the sunlight to be channeled to growth—and recycled at the surface as litter again.

Step more lightly knowing these are underfoot, making a soil which accumulates only fractions of inches in hundreds of years. And wonder at the wisdom of trampling remaining woods even for education, or of paving and building that promise towns in this solitude. How *is* it to be shared without destroying?

One-Flowered Wintergreen / *Moneses uniflora* / PYROLACEAE

Moneses (from the Greek for single delight) is one of comparatively few north woods plants which bloom in mid-summer. Its distribution in the world is circumboreal, in damp coniferous woods and boggy swamps. The star-like waxy flowers *are* a rewarding sight to one who bothers to kneel to their level—a few inches high at most. Each is built perfectly on a pattern of five: five tiny sepals, five petals, five lobes at the tip of the pistil, ten stamens. As with the closely related *Pyrola* species, stamens open to discharge pollen not by splitting down the side, but by a neat round pore at the end. The solitary *Moneses* flowers nod, but as fruits ripen they become erect.

Laws "protecting" wildflowers may be at best symbolic. These have always been bolstered with outright programs of *habitat* preservation, through public acquisition of parks and forests and wilderness, and now nature preserves and scientific areas. But public responsibility for all interesting or wild land seems neither feasible nor desirable. Efforts to regulate the use of such land short of ownership have included, recently, two approaches. Zoning in some jurisdictions has been used to *designate specific areas* as "conservancy," with restrictions on development. Statutes elsewhere have given special protection, through development control boards, for *whole categories of land* defined as fragile.

No less a problem is the protection from over-use, or mis-use, of areas formally given preserve status. Where do you stand, to really look at a Shinleaf? It takes planning, and some regulation, to permit visitors the pleasure both of spotting these wild specimens in the shady summer forest, and of identifying them closeup.

Shinleaf / *Pyrola elliptica* / PYROLACEAE

Several of the rather similar species of *Pyrola* are more or less northern in distribution. *Pyrola elliptica* blooms in mid-summer in deciduous or coniferous woods from Newfoundland to British Columbia, south in the mountains to West Virginia and Arizona. In *P. asarifolia*, flowers are usually pink, the leaves very leathery. *P. virens*, with whitish flowers, has leaves leathery and dark green, blades shorter than their stalks. Characteristic of most species of *Pyrola* is the strongly down-curving style, seen here. In *P. secunda* this is straight, and the white flowers all hang down from an arched upper portion of the stem. Often noticed may be last season's dried stalks, with gray-brown papery capsules discharged of seeds.

Shinleaf

Round-leaved Orchid

Anticipating forest flowers in bloom can add to the pleasure of a walk whenever you take it. Without the stalk of tiny orchids in evidence, could you recognize these glossy, broad leaves as promising something other than *Clintonia* (page 20) or *Smilacina* (page 27)? Then go on to the details that help distinguish superficially similar species of orchids themselves.

Leaves, stems, floral structures; locale; flowering time—all may be important to identification. Sharing part of its range with *Habenaria orbiculata* is *Habenaria hookeri*, HOOKER'S ORCHID. This lacks the reduced leaves (bracts) seen here on the stem, and its flowers have a more tapered and sharp-pointed lip and spur. HOOKER'S ORCHID grows only in the northeastern United States and adjacent Canada. It thrives locally on wooded dunes near the northern Great Lakes with such associates as *Linnaea*, *Clintonia*, and *Calypso*. *H. hookeri* blooms about two weeks earlier than *H. orbiculata* when the two are in the same area.

Round-leaved Orchid / *Habenaria orbiculata* / ORCHIDACEAE

This summer-blooming orchid occurs across the continent from Labrador to southern Alaska, ranging south somewhat beyond the Great Lakes and in the mountains to Georgia. The pair of leaves is strictly basal; there are a very few small reduced leaves or bracts on the stem. The spur is slender, slightly club-shaped, and sometimes over an inch and a half long. Look for *Habernaria orbiculata* in the shade of rich deciduous woods, mixed woods, or coniferous forest—as here, in a grove of WHITE-CEDAR.

There are many species of *Habenaria*. Some, like the fringed ones, have leafy stems and others have leaves all at the base (see page 60). All have the distinctive projecting spur at the base of the lip. In some species, flowers are dull greenish or yellowish, in others white or orange or purple; some have fringed lips and some have simple lips. An even greater variety of color and structure is to be encountered among the estimated 20,000 species in the many other genera of Orchidaceae worldwide.

What accounts for the elaborateness of orchids? Botanists and amateur observers are still piecing together details of the specializations this family exhibits for cross-pollination by *insects*. In contrast, at left in this picture, are the golden-brown spikelets of the TWIG-RUSH, *Cladium mariscoides*, common in wet places from the Great Lakes to Florida. This sedge, lacking colorful petals or nectaries, exposes prominent stigmas that show its adaptation for pollination by *wind*. Notes on many insect pollinators are among the valuable features of the F.S. Mathews *Field Book*, among references, page 71.

Purple Fringed Orchid / *Habenaria psycodes* / ORCHIDACEAE

The lip of this orchid is not only fringed but deeply three-cleft. Occasionally the flowers are pure white. Such albinos may be expected in almost every species with blue, purple, red or pink flowers—including *Iris lacustris*, *Polygala paucifolia*, and *Calopogon pulchellus*, pictured earlier. PURPLE FRINGED ORCHID blooms in summer in a diversity of damp places, thickets, riverbanks, rocky open ground and shores, from Newfoundland to western Ontario, and south in the mountains to Georgia.

Purple Fringed Orchid

Dwarf Rattlesnake-plantain

On first impression, the blooming stalk of this little orchid might be taken for one of the LADIES-TRESSES—pictured on the next page. Some similarities, and the significant differences, may be verified by reference to precise botanical descriptions (e.g. Voss or Case, listed on page 71). Within both genera, *Goodyera* and *Spiranthes*, the several species are sometimes difficult to tell apart, perhaps as the result of hybridization.

But the leaf rosettes of *Goodyera* can be most satisfyingly distinct to the amateur plant-finder, particularly in eastern North America where they bear the mosaic-like markings shown here. Often to be found in large spreading colonies, they remain evergreen through several seasons. The habit of forming offsets from a creeping rhizome gives this species the scientific second name *repens*, but no monopoly on the growth form: three other species of *Goodyera* in North America, whose Latin names happen to refer to characteristics of leaf and flower, are also more or less trailing. A similar habit accounts for the common name, GOLDTHREAD, of the plant whose evergreen leaves are identifiable here: *Coptis trifolia*, seen in flower on page 14. The bristly upright shoots belong to a species of HAIRCAP MOSS, *Polytrichum.*

Dwarf Rattlesnake-plantain / *Goodyera repens* / ORCHIDACEAE

This circumboreal species of *Goodyera* is the smallest of four found across North America. All grow in coniferous and mixed woods. European, northern Canadian and Western American plants usually have plain green leaves; variations in the patterning of leaves here are typical of the eastern American variety *ophioides.* All the species bloom in late summer and early fall.

Insect pollinators and flower adaptations to them remain potentially fruitful subjects for investigation. What better excuse for sitting calmly before a beautiful wild flower and simply looking at it! The GOLDENROD'S pollen, for instance, upon examination appears unlikely to play any role in causing hay fever. But the plants have the misfortune to bloom colorfully at the same time as RAGWEED (*Ambrosia* sp.), whose inconspicuous flowers are the source of great quantities of pollen destined to be windborne. Goldenrod's heavy, sticky pollen grains are better suited for transport on the bodies of jostling beetles and bees.

Watch now at a sunny brookside, bog margin, or between beach ridges, for insect visitors to such late summer bloomers as these characteristic associates of damp, open, often calcareous, ground.

Ohio Goldenrod / *Solidago ohioensis* / COMPOSITAE
Ranging through the region of mixed woods, from New York to Wisconsin, meeting the dark forest at its sunny borders. One of the few GOLDENRODS with the flower cluster flat, a *corymb*. Lower leaves, just visible here, are large and smooth.

Nodding Ladies-tresses / *Spiranthes cernua* / ORCHIDACEAE

Species of LADIES-TRESSES range north, south and west of this one, which is rather common in damp open situations from Newfoundland to North Dakota, south to Florida and Texas. All reward the closer look, their delicate fragrance and floral intricacy reflecting relationships with insects.

Brook Lobelia / *Lobelia kalmii* / CAMPANULACEAE
In damp places, from Newfoundland westward across North America. Also pollinated by insects, as might be expected of any flowers forming so perfect a "landing platform." The tall red *Lobelia cardinalis* is visited by hummingbirds.

Ladies-tresses

Grass-of-Parnassus

Common names have no obligation but to be evocative. "Grass" as used here has the Old Teutonic meaning of the word-root from which it derives: simply, "to grow." Obviously not a grass in the sense of Gramineae, this little herb takes its full name from the Greek mountains, more particularly the summits just north of Delphi, celebrated as a seat of Apollo and the Muses. Said to have been fir-covered and lush with limestone springs, Parnassus was the "type location" for a medicinal plant collected by the Second-Century physician Dioscorides. It may have been *P. palustris.*

With us, *Parnassia* brightens damp calcareous bogs and meadows, shores and hollows. The several species (including a New World variety of *P. palustris*) bloom from July to October. Around the Great Lakes, *Parnassia* is often found on the same shores which in May are colorful with *Primula mistassinica* (page 16) and *Iris lacustris* (page 19). Tall late-summer leaves of the Iris here stand among ripening fruits of the BUNCHBERRY, (page 52), *Cornus canadensis.*

Grass-of-Parnassus / *Parnassia glauca* / SAXIFRAGACEAE

If you look closely at the flower of *Parnassia,* you will see alternating with the stamens a series of candelabrum-shaped structures, each branch tipped with a glistening yellow gland. The different species vary in the shape of these structures (known as *staminodia*), and in leaf texture and shape; all have distinct greenish veins in the petals. *P. glauca* ranges through the northeastern United States west to North Dakota, and adjacent Canada.

Designed by R. Hunter Middleton.
Composition by Monsen Typographers.
Color separations by American Litho Arts.
Printed and bound by R. R. Donnelley & Sons,
The Lakeside Press.

Botanical illustrations and prints

from nature by Torkel Korling

1958 Wild Flowers. Portfolio 16½ x 22 inches. 11 plates. Published and distributed by Container Corporation of America, Chicago. Out of print.

1960 Glory by the Wayside. Book 5 x 7½ inches. 21 plates. Published and distributed by R. R. Donnelley & Sons Company, Chicago. Out of print.

1963 Spring Wild Flowers. Classroom study prints 13 x 18 inches. 8 plates. Society for Visual Education, Chicago.

1963 WILD PLANTS IN FLOWER: plates xlii to xlix. Portfolio 16 x 22 inches. 8 plates.

1966 Second printing, for Field Museum of Natural History, Chicago. 4 plates. Out of print.

WILD PLANTS IN FLOWER: habitat series, with Diane F. Korling, editor.

1972 The Prairie—Swell and Swale

1973 The Boreal Forest and Borders

In preparation:

The Deciduous Woodland
The Prairie—High Plains

Suggestions for Further Reading

Appalachian Mountain Club. 1964. *Mountain Flowers of New England.* Appalachian Mountain Club, Boston.

Bailey, Liberty Hyde. 1933. *How Plants Get Their Names.* The Macmillan Company. Republished in paper, 1963, Dover Publications, New York.

Case, Frederick W., Jr. 1964. *Orchids of the Western Great Lakes Region.* Cranbrook Institute of Science, Bloomfield Hills, Michigan.

Courtenay, Booth, and James H. Zimmerman. 1972. *Wildflowers and Weeds.* (With color plates.) Van Nostrand Reinhold, New York.

Curtis, John T. 1959. *The Vegetation of Wisconsin: An Ordination of Plant Communities.* University of Wisconsin Press, Madison.

Dorr, John A., and Donald F. Eschman. 1970. *Geology of Michigan.* University of Michigan Press, Ann Arbor.

Fernald, Merritt Lyndon, and Alfred Charles Kinsey, Revised by Reed C. Rollins. 1958. *Edible Wild Plants of Eastern North America.* Harper & Row, New York.

Fernald, Merritt Lyndon. 1950. *Gray's Manual of Botany.* Eighth Edition. American Book Company, New York.

Gleason, Henry A., and Arthur Cronquist. 1963. *Manual of Vascular Plants of Northeastern United States and Adjacent Canada.* D. Van Nostrand Company, Inc., Princeton, N.J.

Gleason, Henry A., and Arthur Cronquist. 1964. *The Natural Geography of Plants.* Columbia University Press, New York.

Hultén, Eric. 1968. *Flora of Alaska and Neighboring Territories.* Stanford University Press, Stanford.

Kingsbury, John M. 1964. *Poisonous Plants of the United States and Canada.* Prentice-Hall, Inc., Englewood Cliffs, New Jersey.

Knauth, Percy, and the Editors of Time-Life Books. 1972. *The North Woods.* Time, Inc., New York.

Lawrence, George H. M. 1955. *Introduction to Plant Taxonomy.* The Macmillan Company, New York.

Mathews, F. Schuyler. 1902. *Field Book of American Wild Flowers.* G. P. Putnam's Sons, New York. (In current editions.)

McCormick, Jack. 1966. *The Life of the Forest.* McGraw-Hill Book Company, New York.

Montgomery, F. H. 1962. *Native Wild Plants of Eastern Canada and the Adjacent Northeastern United States.* Ryerson Press, Toronto.

Voss, Edward G. 1972. *Michigan Flora, Part I, Gymnosperms and Monocots.* Cranbrook Institute of Science, Bloomfield Hills, Michigan.

Watts, Mae Theilgaard. 1957. *Reading the Landscape: An Adventure in Ecology.* The Macmillan Company, New York.

Index to Plants Pictured and Mentioned

Bold face indicates major illustration subjects. Numbers refer to text pages in every case.